# Trixie,
## My Shetland Pony

by
Dr. Edward Keller

*as it was in years past,*

*Best Wishes!*

*Dr Edward Keller*

**Early Dakota Prairie Series**

MY EARLY DAKOTA PRAIRIE LIFE
Books By Dr. Edward Keller
1732 Golf Drive
Bismarck, ND 58503
701-223-5302
www.lasercrafts.com

# Preface

"Trixie, My Shetland Pony" is a story
about Dr. Keller's
first horse on their early Dakota prairie farm.
The time is the 1930's in Strasburg, North Dakota.

Keller creates a memory story of this special
relationship between boy and animal during his
early years on the family farm.

# Dedication

*This book is dedicated to horse lovers of all ages and to our sixteen grandchildren, especially to our grandson, Brian Keller.*

Dr. Edward Keller

Inquiries about this book should be addressed to:
Edward F. Keller, 529 2nd Avenue West,
Dickinson, North Dakota 58601
701-225-5302

ISBN 0-9660833-7-7

Printed and bound in the United States of America

# Trixie,
## My Shetland Pony

by
Dr. Edward Keller

*illustrations by David Christy*

When I was a little boy on my
Strasburg, North Dakota farm in the
1930's I had a little Shetland pony
named Trixie.

I got Trixie from our

good neighbors the

Ebach family.

My father traded a

burlap sack full of wheat

and a female calf for

Trixie.

We drove to Ebach's

in a wagon

with the wheat and

the calf to get Trixie.

I was very

excited as I rode

the pony home.

Trixie's little head

had tiny ears

and his little bridle

had a tiny bit for his

mouth.

His hooves made cute
little tracks on the dirt
and snow.

I was taller than Trixie and it

was easy for me to mount him.

Trixie and I spent

much time together

and we became

friends.

We gathered the cows from the pasture for milking.

We gathered the horses when my
father needed them for farm work.

Some Sundays I visited my

neighbors with Trixie.

Trixie and I fetched the mail

from the mail box a mile away.

Trixie made tricks for the mailman

and made him laugh.

Trixie could stand

on his hind legs

with me on his

back.

He could also

raise his right leg

to shake hands

with me.

Trixie loved to go swimming

with me in my farm stock dam.

He loved walking into the water

and swimming to the other side

with me on his back.

It was a very smooth ride.

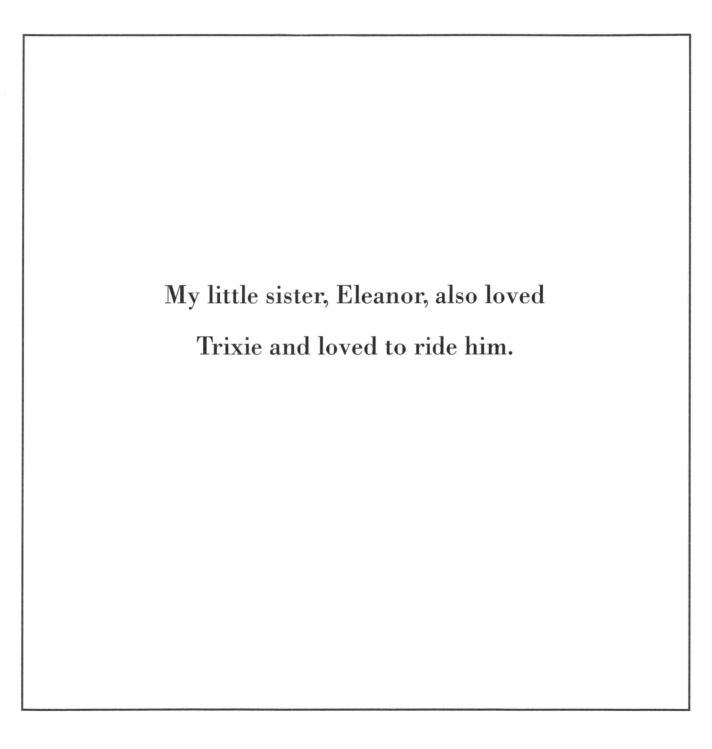

My little sister, Eleanor, also loved

Trixie and loved to ride him.

If she fell off Trixie,

he would stop, turn to her and

nuzzle her as she sat on the ground.

Then Eleanor would lead Trixie

to a large rock, a fence or tree

stump and get back on him again.

I never used a saddle when

I rode Trixie.  I liked

the closeness to his skin

and to feel his movements.

Besides in the winter Trixie's
warm body and thick winter
hair felt good.

It was so much fun

caring for Trixie.

He enjoyed it when I petted him and curried his coat and gave him oats and water.

I felt so happy that Trixie was my very

own pony and we were such good friends.

# Trixie, My Shetland Pony

When I was a little boy on my Strasburg, North Dakota farm in the 1930's I had a little Shetland pony named Trixie.

I got Trixie from our good neighbors the Ebach family. My father traded a burlap sack full of wheat and a female calf for Trixie. We drove to Ebach's in a wagon with the wheat and the calf to get Trixie. I was very excited as I rode the pony home.

Trixie's little head had tiny ears and his little bridle had a tiny bit for his mouth. His hooves made cute little tracks on the dirt and snow. I was taller than Trixie and it was easy for me to mount him.

Trixie and I spent much time together and we became friends. We gathered the cows from the pasture for milking. We gathered the horses when my father needed them for farm work. Some Sundays I visited my neighbors with Trixie. Trixie and I fetched the mail from the mail box a mile away. Trixie made tricks for the mailman and made him laugh.

Trixie could stand on his hind legs with me on his back. He could also raise his right leg to shake hands with me.

Trixie loved to go swimming with me in my farm stock dam. He loved walking into the water and swimming to the other side with me on his back. It was a very smooth ride.

My little sister, Eleanor, also loved Trixie and loved to ride him. If she fell off Trixie, he would stop, turn to her and nuzzle her as she sat on the ground. Then Eleanor would lead Trixie to a large rock, a fence or tree stump and get back on him again.

I never used a saddle when I rode Trixie. I liked the closeness to his skin and to feel his movements. Besides in the winter Trixie's warm body and thick winter hair felt good.

It was so much fun caring for Trixie. He enjoyed it when I petted him and curried his coat and gave him oats and water. I felt so happy that Trixie was my very own pony and we were such good friends.

## "My First Grade, 1932"

"My First Grade, 1932" is a story about Dr. Keller's first year in school. Getting to school from their prairie farm in Strasburg, North Dakota was an adventure itself. Keller weaves a memory

story of his siblings and neighbor children getting to and from school along with the events of a typical school day. The hard cover, 56 page children's history picture book is 8x8 inches in full color. Artist illustrator, David Christy, fills each page with color pictures of little Ed and his school mates attending that first year at his country school house. Various anecdotal pictures throughout the book complete the setting for "My First Grade, 1932."

Heading to school in the Keller school bus: "We drive the three miles in a sled or buggy with Dave and Tootsy."

*All Ages.*
*Self published 2003, 56 - 8x8 pages, hardcover, $12.00.*
*ISBN 0-9660833-6-9*

## "My Mother's Apron"

"My Mother's Apron" is a story about Dr. Keller's mother and the apron she wore daily on their early prairie farm in the 1930's in Strasburg, North Dakota. Keller creates a compelling image of his mother and her home made apron.

Always present with everything his mother did, the apron was more than just a garment to be worn. It was an incredible tool used for a wide variety of tasks. The hard cover, 56 page children's history picture book is 8x8 inches in full color. Artist illustrator, David Christy, paints 28 pictures of Keller's mother with her apron. Christy captures the facial expressions from actual archival photographs of her. Additional anecdotal pictures create a living history of the 1930's farmstead home.

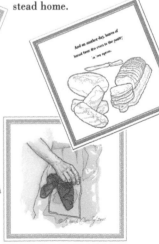

Early Dakota Prairie Series

*For ages 1 to 101.*
*Self published 2001, 56 - 8x8 pages, hardcover, $12.00.*
*ISBN 0-9660833-5-0*

## "Memory Stories"...

In 95 short vignettes, like "My Mother's Apron", "Horse Power", "Welk is Here", "The Watkins Man", "Prairie Humor", Keller evokes the wholesome, sacrificing spirit of his ancestors in the 1930's on the Dakota prairies, the honorable use of what nature provided and the far-reaching effects of faith.

*Self published 1997, large print, 158 - 8½ x11 pages, perfect bound paperback, $12.00. ISBN 0-9660833-1-8*

## Audio Cassette Book-"Memory Stories"...

90 minute, 33 story cassette tape, read by Earl Ackerman, radio personality, KRRB FM, Dickinson, North Dakota.

*Self published 1998, $12.00. ISBN 0-9660833-2-6*

## "Memory Stories II"...

In 94 short vignettes Keller details his early childhood. In stories like "My Best Ice Cream Ever", "My Father's Lap", "Sugar Bread", "Dakota Gypsies", "My Table", Keller's early prairie experiences come alive.

*Self published 1999, large print, 134 - 8½ x11 pages, perfect bound paperback, $12.00. ISBN 0-9660833-3-4*

## "My First World"...

In "My First World" Keller tells of growing up near Strasburg and Linton, North Dakota in the 1930's. At the time Lawrence Welk was a rising star accordionist from Strasburg. Keller chronicles his German Russian ancestors from Germany to Russia to Strasburg, how they worked the land, attended schools, church, parties, dances during the Great Depression, drought and grasshoppers on the early prairies.

*Self published 1995, large print, 76 - 8½ x11 pages, plus 9 pages of maps and pictures, perfect bound paperback, $12.00. ISBN 0-9660833-0-X*

All the books can be obtained in bookstores, from www.lasercrafts.com or ordered directly from the author:

- ☐ Trixie, My Shetland Pony . . . . . . . . . . . . . $12.00
- ☐ My First Grade, 1932 . . . . . . . . . . . . . . . . $12.00
- ☐ My Mother's Apron . . . . . . . . . . . . . . . . . . $12.00
- ☐ My First World . . . . . . . . . . . . . . . . . . . . $12.00
- ☐ Memory Stories . . . . . . . . . . . . . . . . . . . . $12.00
- ☐ Memory Stories audio cassette . . . . . . . . . $12.00
- ☐ Memory Stories II . . . . . . . . . . . . . . . . . . $12.00
- ☐ Amateur Writer . . . . . . . . . . . . . . . . . . . . $12.00
- ☐ Audio Cassette German Russian Waltzes & Polkas . . $11.00
  played by Bob Dolajak (Music Lawrence Welk played as a young man)

Please add $2.00 Shipping & Handling per order.

Mail to: Dr. Edward F. Keller, 529 2nd Ave. W., Dickinson, ND 58601
Phone: (701) 225-5302

*Early Dakota Prairie Series*